MORE

BRIl
ADVICE!

MORE

BRILLIANT

ADVICE!

by Annie Lawson

A Deirdre McDonald Book

BELLEW PUBLISHING

London

First published in 1989
by Deirdre McDonald Books
Bellew Publishing Co. Ltd.
7 Southampton Place, London WC1A 2DR

Copyright © by Annie Lawson 1989

All rights reserved

ISBN 0 947792 24 4

Printed in Hong Kong by
Regent Publishing Services Ltd

This book is sold subject to the condition that it shall not,
by way of trade or otherwise, be lent, re-sold, hired out,
or otherwise circulated without the Publisher's prior
consent in any form of binding or cover other than that in
which it is published and without a similar condition
including this condition being imposed on the
subsequent purchaser.

brown rice!
OH NO!
muesli!
YERK!
kaftans!
lentil stew!
YIK!
tahini!
Donovan!
painted vans!
OW!
breastfeeding!
RETCH!
just a minute... we believe in that

3 wet lettuces
You never meet anybody at things like this!
It's too crowded for me!
Theres no one here! Lets go!
go dancing

LAST SUMMER, ANDREW GREW HIS HAIR SHOULDER-LENGTH AT THE BACK...
Suddenly, he was pursued by FEMALE CHAUVINISTS...
ANDREW'S looking very ATTRACTIVE these days... HMM?!!! what's happened?
YES! what IS it? Did he used to have a moustache? Was it glasses?
It was amazing!...
oh I love your HAIR like that Andrew! You look so SEXY!!
!
Until...
oh you're so DISHY you look like a 60's POP STAR! In a month there'll be enough for a pony tail! You look like Andrew Ridgley out of WHAM! I love that bit that curls in your ear
SHIT
Later...
Growing my hair must be the naff-est thing I ever did in 1984
GONE
I don't understand it! Why don't they want to look attractive?

You know what Barbara told me yesterday ... she gets a SERVICE wash done at the launderette!
She DOESN'T!!
What's wrong with that?
She DOES! she told me!
That's disgusting! EXPLOITATION!!
I'd like to hear how she justifies that!
Right! I expect that launderette woman gets about £15 for a 60-hour week!
Well they get paid extra for service...
TERRIBLE! I could never have anyone washing my clothes for me...could you?
Did you say something Lesley?
Yes... other people's washing... ...it's a dirty business!

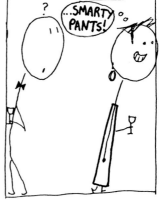

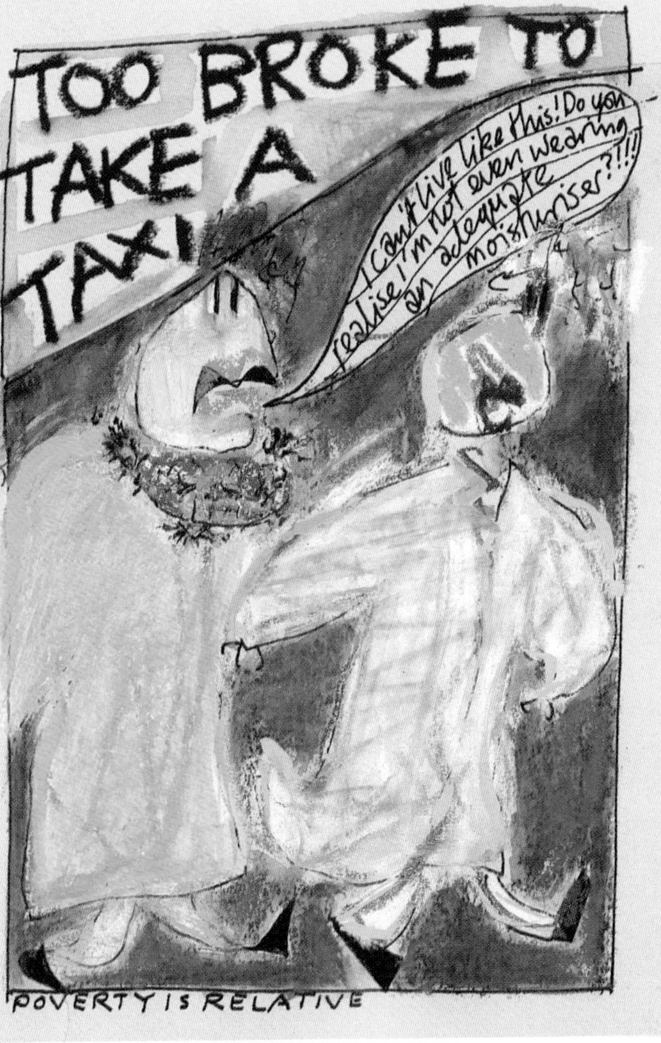

POVERTY IS RELATIVE

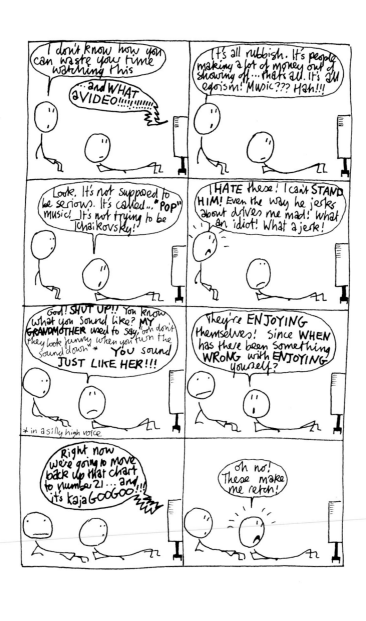

Jane sometimes listens to WINNIE TAMMETTE ...
I always have a good laugh at this!
WINNIE TAM-METTE
Today a posse of women came to see me...
...To make me realise women don't have equal rights. But they went when I told them... I feel equal ...to an angel...
...when my man holds me at night...
My man he treats me like a baby And he's so gentle and so nice to me.....
What's this crap?
Shut up Simon!
So I do all I can to please him... cos my man works hard & takes good care of me....
God... This is TERRIBLE!
DON'T LIB-ER-ATE ME... JUST LOVE ME...
How can you CALL YOURSELF A FEMINIST AND LISTEN TO THIS RUBBISH?!
Cos I'm as free as I'll ever want to be. Some women just cain't understand ...there's quite a lot of difference...
It's fantasy
What? You want to be like THAT?!
...between a woman and a man... And I just know that's the way God meant it to be...
NO!
SOME women take this SERIOUSLY!...
So love me and don't lib-er-ate me...
...in MILTON KEYNES!
oh fuck off!

IT'S THE FASHIONABLE THING NOWADAYS FOR OLDER WOMEN TO GO OUT WITH YOUNGER MEN, FOR:-
CHINESE BURNS
DEAD-LEGS
"HORSEBITES"
PARALYSING NECK-GRIPS
...OR THE EMOTIONAL EQUIVALENTS

POST-FEMINIST MAN
FLEES FEMALE IN
SQUEAMISH FRENZY!

period

Going home....
Another boring night of TV ahead I expect...
I wonde what's on...
I wish my social life was better...
...I wish I was going out with "Minder"!
The GUARDIAN

We have to acknowledge ...that there IS something between us...
This strange magnetism ...all consuming..
The more it burns the more it grows...
AND THERE ARE TIMES WHEN I'M AWARE OF NOTHING ELSE!
IT'S so HUGE! ..THIS FEELING!
I've been in love twice before..
liar

GLOOM
Something has to happen soon. I CAN'T GO ON!
I hate my work
...and RELATIONSHIPS? SCREAM! DON'T MAKE ME LAUGH!
SELF PITY
AH! Time for "DALLAS"!
Sue Ellen, your marriage to J.R. is desparately unhappy. Why don't you quit?
No Jenna! I've somehow coped up to now! Maybe I'll try separate bedrooms
HAPPY
...but there's some-thing missing...
THERE'S THIS GREAT HOLLOW IN MY LIFE...

Assertiveness Training

I WOULDN'T EVEN GIVE HIM THE STEAM FROM MY PISS!

TOM was at his girlfriend's, JULIA had an important meeting, and HELEN had stopped in the previous week for the gas people. So when NELSON had his EYE, it was down to IAN to take him to the vet...
I STILL say HELEN should have! she's got a CAR for god's sake!
TEAR! RATTLE!
KARRY-PET BOX
SCRABBLE!
WAITING ROOM
What have you got in there? A kitten?
Yes. It's only got one eye! It had an abcess behind the other and scratched it out at birth. Now it's gone septic!
SICK
GREEN
Oh... poor little thing! Best have it put down eh?
KARRY-PET BOX
MIEOW!
Hmf! Maybe!
...and TOM should make his mind up where he's living!... I may be un-employed but I've still got THINGS TO DO! It wasn't MY decision to get a cat! JULIA! It's JULIA's respons-ibility! But JULIA is at a MEETING! "Let's RESCUE the poor little ONE-EYED RUNT," she goes! The bloody thing will be RUNNING ROUND IN CIRCLES...
KARRY-PET BOX
But... will it be able to lead a normal life, vet?
Oh yes! I'll give him a course of antibiotics to clear up the infection and he'll be as right as rain!
PLEASED AS A CAT WITH 2 TAILS

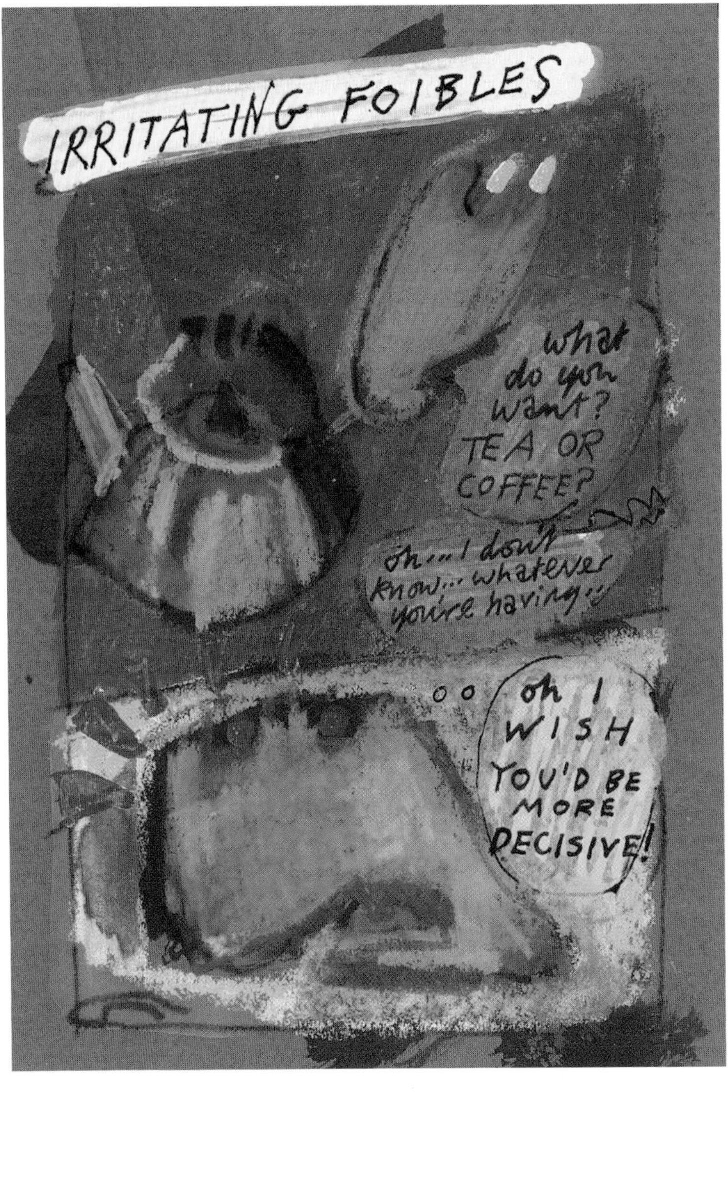
IRRITATING FOIBLES
what do you want? TEA OR COFFEE?
oh... I don't know... whatever you're having...
oh I WISH YOU'D BE MORE DECISIVE!

Honestly Alison, I'm continually flabbergasted at your total lack of knowledge! You're the most POLITICALLY IGNORANT person I know!
I bet you don't even know who NEIL KINNOCK is! Come on... who's Neil Kinnock?
That's not fair! I AM political...
...I HATE THE QUEEN!!!
Alison... you hate THE QUEEN because you don't like her HAIRSTYLE! Come on... WHO'S NEIL KINNOCK?
I don't hate the queen's hairstyle! I HATE PRINCESS DI'S HAIRSTYLE!!!
It's no reason not to like someone just because you don't like their HAIR-STYLE ALISON!
God, you're so shallow! How can I know you? It's embarrassing!
Anyway... I do know who Neil Kinnock is.. he's someone in the government!
oh WELL DONE! 10 out of 10!!!!!!
CLAP
I made an interesting observation the other day Alison.. Have you noticed that Princess Di's hairstyle is the same as that bloke's in WHAM?
what's wham?

Do you think SIMON will be at Sonia's party?
I don't know...
I have to face it! I'm forced to bump into him sooner or later so there's no point in hiding round corners!
Otherwise he'd still be ruling my life wouldn't he? If he says, "Hello! Long time no see!" I'LL say, "NOT LONG ENOUGH YOU CREEP!"
...or I might say... "If it wasn't such a timeworn cliché you'd get this drink in your face PAL!!"
that's good!
or... "As far as I'M concerned, Simon, YOU'RE DEAD. So please remove your DEAD BODY from where I'm standing!" Hey...that's good!
No, come to think of it I won't say anything! I'll just STARE THROUGH him as if he's invisible! That's the best don't you think?
um...
Later.. at SONIA'S PARTY...
HE'S NOT HERE!! I had this whole speech worked out!
Well, as far as I know he doesn't know Sonia does he?

I'm pissed off. I thought Simon would be here and he's not. Do you think he knows about it?
Do you think he didn't come because he knew I was coming? Is he avoiding me?
maybe he didn't know about it though
OH GOD! Why are you bothered about SIMON? SIMON'S just a BLOB!
In fact ALL these people are BORING BLOBS!
Simon isn't a blob!
WE need to meet some INTERESTING NEW PEOPLE!
Yes he is! He's got a blob mentality! You need to WIDEN YOUR CIRCLE!
Well maybe I LIKE BLOBS!
AND MAYBE I'M A BLOB!
oh how disgusting!
I wish I was a member of the "GROOVIBAR CLUB"!

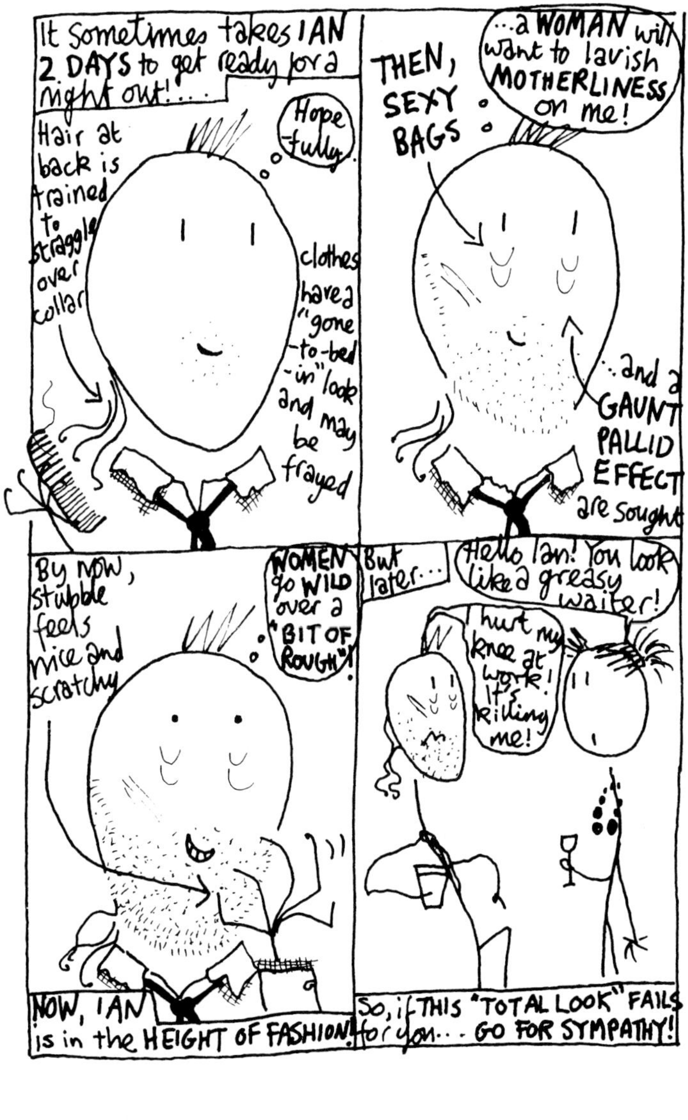
It sometimes takes IAN 2 DAYS to get ready for a night out!....
Hope-fully.
Hair at back is trained to straggle over collar
clothes have a "gone-to-bed-in" look and may be frayed
THEN, SEXY BAGS
...a WOMAN will want to lavish MOTHERLINESS on me!
...and a GAUNT PALLID EFFECT are sought
By now, stubble feels nice and scratchy
WOMEN go WILD over a "BIT OF ROUGH"!
NOW, IAN is in the HEIGHT OF FASHION!
But later...
Hello Ian! You look like a greasy waiter!
I hurt my knee at work! It's killing me!
So, if THIS "TOTAL LOOK" FAILS for you... GO FOR SYMPATHY!

You'll never guess what happened when I went to the bar... SOME MAN PINCHED MY BUM!!!
oh no! They didn't!
I'm livid! I feel INVADED! Problem is, I don't know who it was!
Well it's typical! What a cretin! The world's full of creeps + bastards!
It's typical isn't it
Yes fucking typical. Typical of the political situation...
Oh bloody hell! Aren't we getting rather off the point?
WHAT DO YOU MEAN?
SOME people can't afford to bloody EAT that's what! Let's worry about THAT, instead of griping about inconsequential flotsam! Typical feminists, bogged down in trivia!
Well that's the biggest CROCK OF CRAP I've heard in my entire life! Personal/political acts such as this are microcosms of world-wide issues don't you realise?!!!!!!
I completely agree! For instance, that bloke could be CRUISE MISSILES and MOLESWORTH Thingummy's bum...
Last orders please!

I'm rather glad celibacy is fashionable nowadays

Well.. let me think ..I know! Maybe you should get to know the particular woman concerned WELL enough, so that you know which approach would be most success-ful...
...Also, find out what mood she's in that day, as the type of thing one wants on one day may be completely different to what one wants on another..
But that's just IT isn't it?!!! They keep changing their MINDS! That's what I'm SAYING!
Why can't they be CONSTANT like MEN? Men always want the SAME! Men are SIMPLE!
But... I think that FINDING OUT about a person is the most exciting part of a relation-ship! It's, really INTERESTING!
D...oh! I'm too old!
What?..Too old for FLIRTING?
d...oh!

That girl must have hurt herhead!
hee hee hee!
ho ho!
hmm...
glad I'm a
REAL PERSON

THE DAY BEFORE SUSIE LEFT HE SAT IN THE BATH + LOOKED AT ALL THE COSMETIC BOTTLES, TOMORROW THEY WOULD BE GONE!

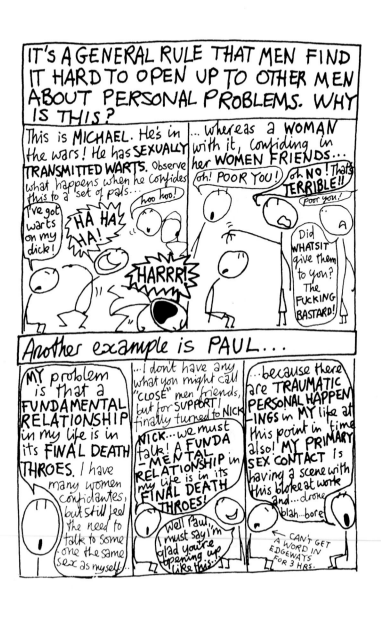

KETTLE'S FUCKED

WET LETTUCE
I'm feeling down
I wonder why?
maybe it's the crappy weather
or maybe it's that I'm not living with a wildly attractive intellectually stimulating wise caring EROTIC human being who makes me laugh 100% of the time...
..and who doesn't invade my space.
WAIL
YEAH
MUSING

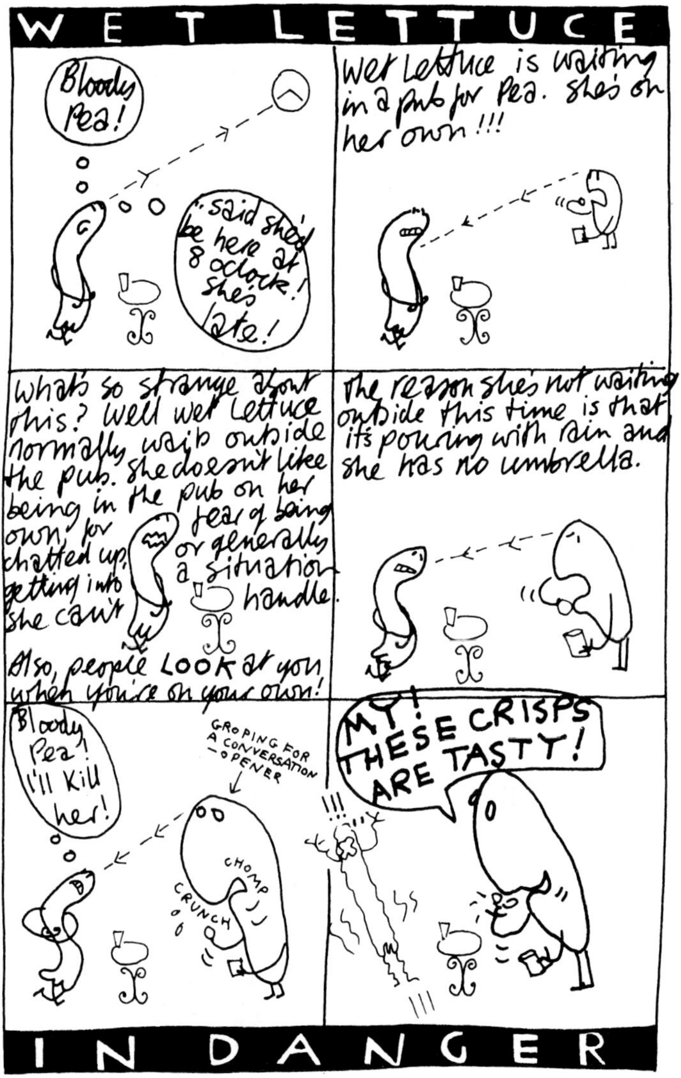
WET LETTUCE
Bloody Pea!
...said she'd be here at 8 o'clock! She's late!
Wet Lettuce is waiting in a pub for Pea. She's on her own!!!
What's so strange about this? Well Wet Lettuce normally waits outside the pub. She doesn't like being in the pub on her own, for fear of being chatted up, or generally getting into a situation she can't handle.
Also, people LOOK at you when you're on your own!
The reason she's not waiting outside this time is that it's pouring with rain and she has no umbrella.
Bloody Pea! I'll kill her!
GROPING FOR A CONVERSATION OPENER
CHOMP
CRUNCH
MY! THESE CRISPS ARE TASTY!
IN DANGER

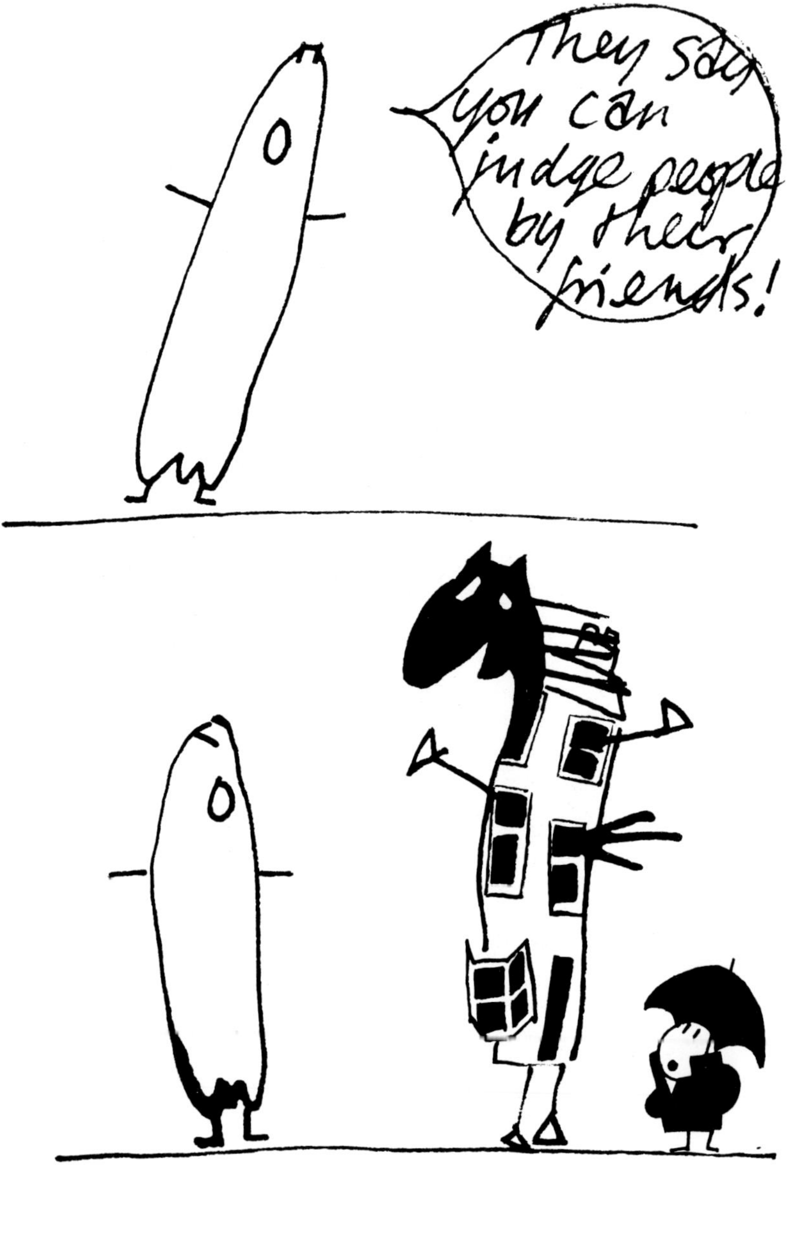
They say you can judge people by their friends!

I've GOT to find a way to make a living!

WILD-HORSE-IN-A-HOUSE

GETS THE IDEA OF DIPPING FLEAS IN CHOCOLATE + SELLING THEM AT CAMDEN LOCK.